'Even the light that emanates from precious gemstones cannot compare to the colourful light of blooming flowers. Every conceivable flame, light, glow, and shade of colour is exhibited by blossoming flowers.' – Gustav Klimt

The Belvedere museum, in Vienna, houses the world's largest collection of oil paintings by Gustav Klimt, one of the most famous Austrian painters. His artistic development is especially visible in the Belvedere – portraits, allegorical paintings and landscapes show us how Klimt has processed various influences in his work, from Historicism through the Vienna Secession up to his later avant-garde work. With this official colouring book, *Colour Your Own Klimt*, you will embark on an artistic exploration!

As co-founder of the Vienna Secession movement, Klimt was primarily dedicated to the innovation of the arts. In this colouring book we have brought together some of his world-famous women's portraits, from the early portrait of *Sonja Knips* up to the refined portrayal of *Fritza Riedler*. The use of materials and the energy radiating from the shiny golden background is as marvellous as his best-known work, the allegorical-symbolic *The Kiss*. The ornamental estheticism of his landscapes, in as the *Cottage Garden* with *Sunflowers*, and the *Avenue to Schloss Kammer Park* is also evident.

With this exclusive colouring book for adults you can create your own piece of art, your very own Klimt! Colouring is not just soothing, above all it helps you relax and feel good. Concentrating on your pencil, choosing the colours, using lighter and darker accents – colouring provides you with new strength and energy.

Colouring can also be meditative – stress and worries disappear and you will learn how to leave things behind, how to experiment. Colouring is also a technique that can be valued in its own right. Come closer to yourself and this great artists, get out your pencils and get started.

Portrait of Adele Bloch-Bauer I (1907)

Cottage Garden with Sunflowers (1906)

The Kiss (1907)

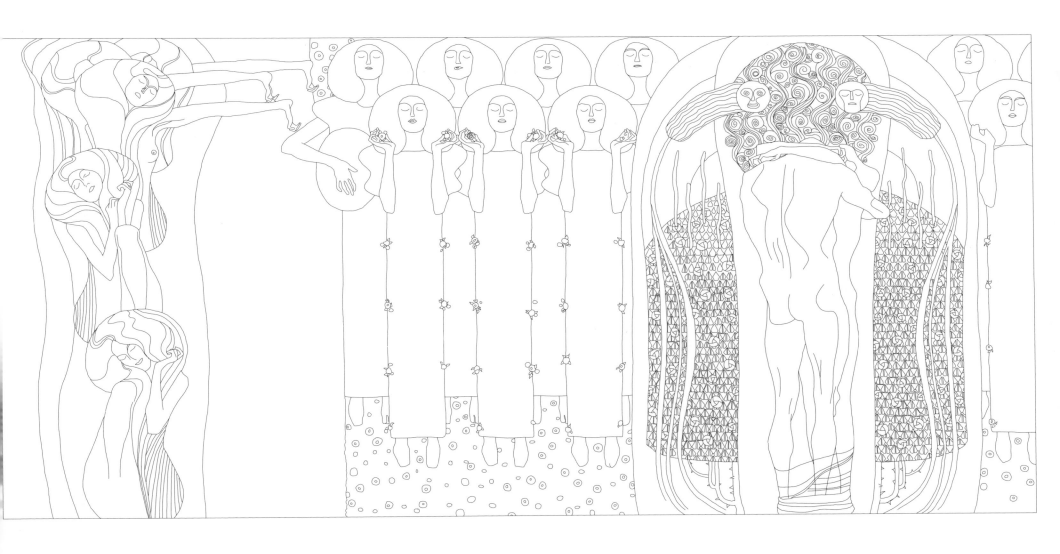

The Beethoven Frieze: The Arts, Chorus of Paradise, Embrace (1901–1902)

Houses in Unterach on Lake Attersee (1916)

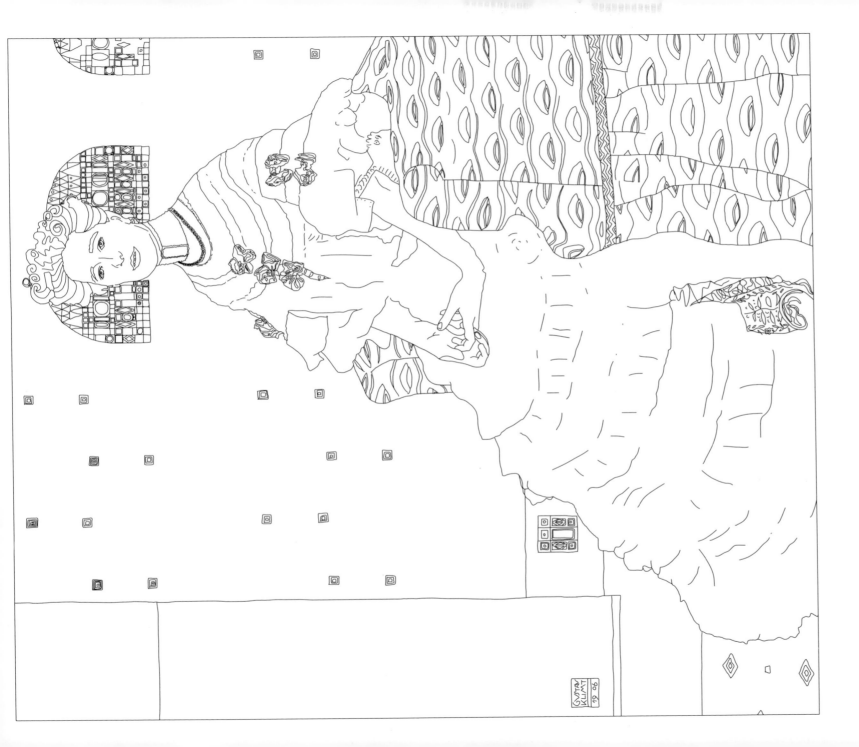

Fritza Riedler (1906)

Lake Attersee (1900)

Hygieia (Detail from Faculty Paintings: Medicine) (1900)

Lady with Fan (1917)

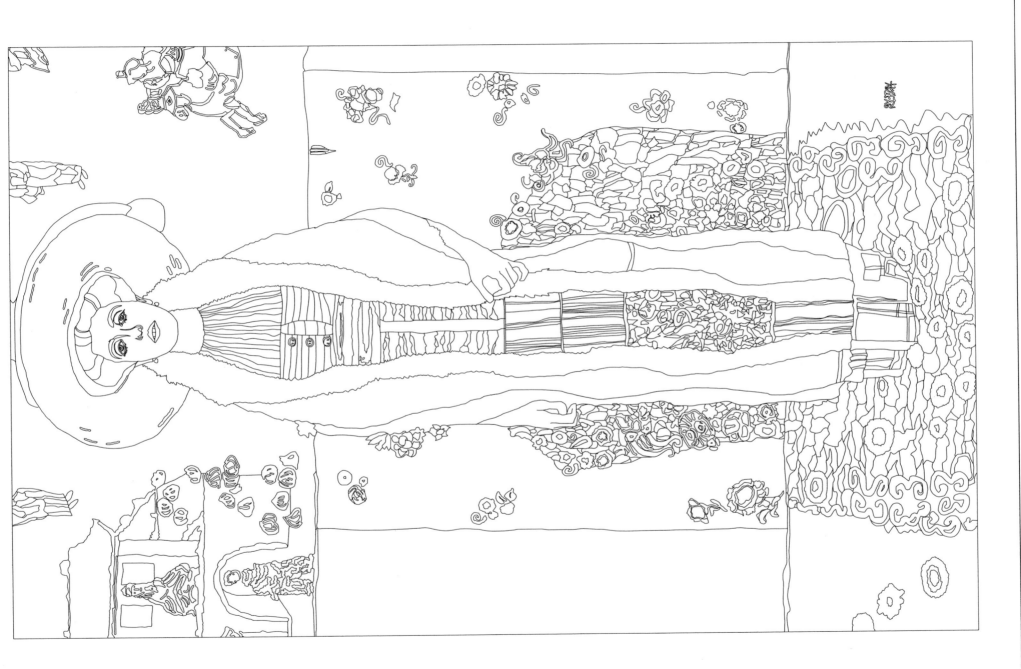

Portrait of Adele Bloch-Bauer II (1912)

Schloss Kammer on Lake Attersee III (1909–1910)

Judith I (1901)

Lady with Hat and Feather Boa (1909)

The Family (1909)

Water Serpents II (1904)

Sonja Knips (1897–1898)

Johanna Staude (1917)

Avenue to Schloss Kammer Park (1912)

Farmhouse in Buchberg (1911)

The Bride (1917–1918)

Blooming Poppies (1907)

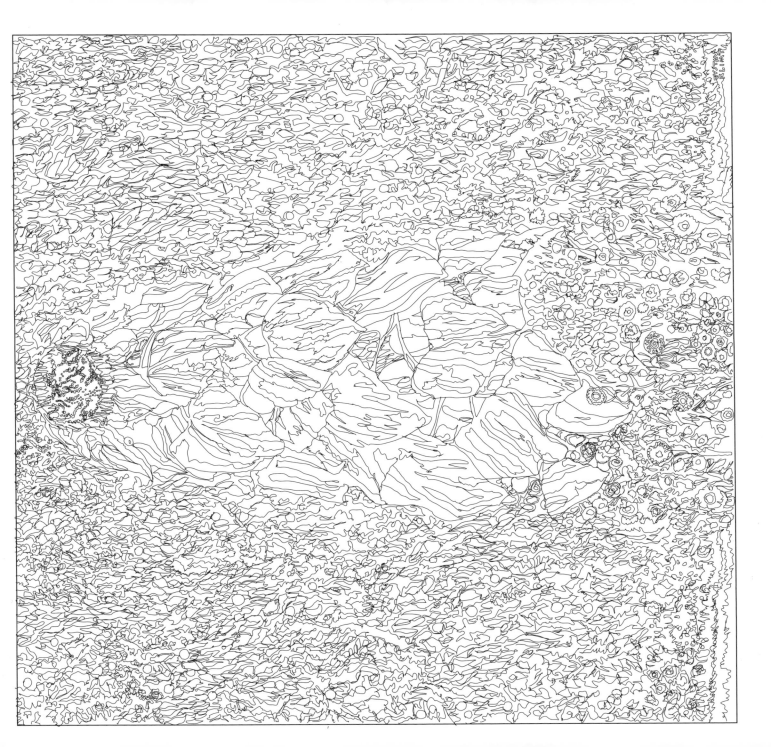

Sunflower (1907-1908)